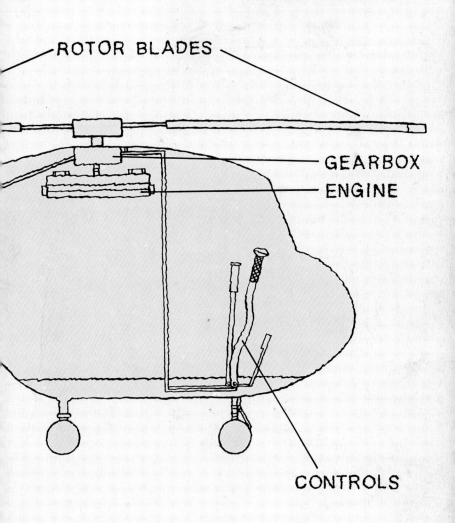

ROTOR BLADES

GEARBOX

ENGINE

CONTROLS

Published exclusively for
J Sainsbury plc
Stamford Street London SE1 9LL
by Walker Books Ltd
184-192 Drummond Street
London NW1 3HP

First published 1985
Reprinted 1985

Text © 1985 Arlene Blanchard
Illustrations © 1985 Tony Wells

ISBN 0-7445-0405-8

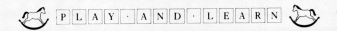

The Helicopter

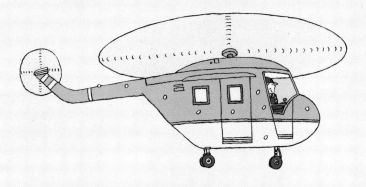

Written by Arlene Blanchard
Illustrated by Tony Wells

SAINSBURY'S · WALKER BOOKS

'This is Oil Rig 2. This is Oil Rig 2. We have an emergency. A steel girder has fallen on a man's leg.

Can you come to help?'
Sam the helicopter pilot hears the
message on his short-wave radio.

He hurries outside to the helipad, where his helicopter, Dragonfly 1, is waiting.

The engine roars. The rotor blades
whirr. Lift off!
They're on their way.

Sam sees the oil rig ahead of him. No ship can get there in this storm.

He hovers above the rig looking for the mark that tells him where to land.

'Quick, over here!'
Sam hurries to where Joe is trapped
and hooks a rope round the girder.

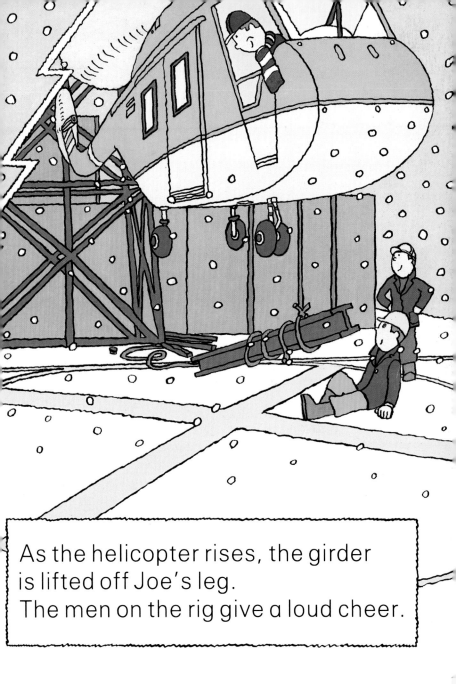

As the helicopter rises, the girder
is lifted off Joe's leg.
The men on the rig give a loud cheer.

Joe's leg looks badly bruised. Two men carry him to the helicopter.

Sam wants to get him to the hospital quickly.

As they fly towards the land, Sam sees a small boat in trouble. He flies low and drops a rope.

The fishermen fasten it to their boat.
Dragonfly 1 pulls the boat into
safe water close to shore.

The snow is getting thicker.
'We can't land here,' Sam says
as they fly over the coast.

'There's too much snow.
I'll radio to the hospital
that we'll go straight there.'

They soon see the hospital ahead of them. A man has cleared a space in the car-park.

'This will do.' Sam smiles as
he prepares to land Dragonfly 1.

As the helicopter comes down, the rotor blades blow more snow off the tarmac.

A nurse and doctor hurry out to help Joe. It's not every day a patient arrives by helicopter.

As Sam flies off, a message comes over the radio. The farm tractor can't get out to feed the sheep.

Sam and Dragonfly 1 are needed.
'I'm so glad to see you,' Farmer Jack
says as Sam arrives.

The helicopter lifts the bales of hay high into the air. Sam turns in the direction of the hills.

Sam climbs out of the cockpit.
'We're a good team,' he says.
'What would they do without us?'

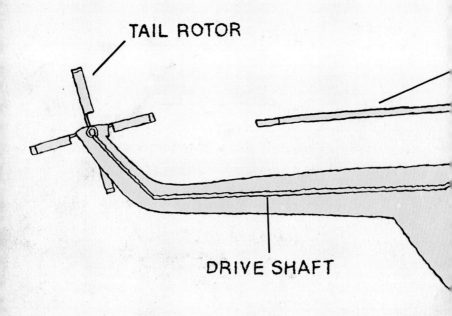

TAIL ROTOR

DRIVE SHAFT

DRAGONFLY 1